WITNESS

Norman Matheis

Sydney J. Hielema

Dordt College Press, Sioux Center, Iowa

#75 "By the Powers for Good: December 1944", p. 522 from *A TESTAMENT TO FREEDOM*: *THE ESSENTIAL WRITINGS OF DIETRICH BONHOEFFER* by GEFFREY B. KELLY and F. BURTON NELSON (EDS.) Copyright © 1991 by Geffrey B. Kelly and F. Burton Nelson. Reprinted by permission of HarperCollins Publishers Inc.

Printed in the United States of America.

Dordt College Press   www.dordt.edu/dordt_press
498 Fourth Avenue NE
Sioux Center, Iowa 51250
United States of America
ISBN: 0-932914-55-1

The Library of Congress Cataloging-in-Publication Data
is on file with the Library of Congress, Washington, D.C.

Library of Congress Control Number: 2004104251

Dedication

For Jeff, Ellen and Ken, with love, N.M.

Foreword

During this Jubilee year, Dordt College celebrates the vision of its founders and their determination to establish a pervasively Christian institution of higher education in the American heartland. We also celebrate the work of students, faculty, staff, and supporters whose persistent diligence has continued this vision.

Witness puts our celebration into perspective. As Jesus told his eager disciples who wanted to get busy building the kingdom under the leadership of their risen Lord, "That's not your task. Your task is to wait for the Holy Spirit. And it is the Spirit who will give you power, not as builders but as witnesses to the kingdom that I will bring." That's what this book is about.

From Abraham to Sojourner Truth, the people represented in these pages remind us that it is through the faith–filled witness of Spirit-filled disciples that the Savior's kingdom reveals itself among us now. So also, from Elijah to Blaise Pascal, the text and portraits in this book remind us that our most far-sighted founders, generous supporters, energetic staff, and gifted academicians together could never really become the *builders* of the academic community known today as Dordt College. At best—and it was their best—they were faithful *witnesses* to the sovereign reign of a cosmic redeemer who now declares that there really is not any square inch in all of creation that does not belong to him.

The past years show clearly that our covenant Lord is faithful. The future holds the promise of new opportunities for kingdom service. Consider this publication Dordt College's testimony to the first 50 years of God's calling and as a promise of our continued faithful witness during the next half century of our academic service—or for as many years as the Lord gives us until he comes again.

Dr. Carl E. Zylstra
President, Dordt College
July 2004

Preface

Therefore, since we are surrounded by such a great cloud of witnesses, let us throw off everything that hinders and the sin that so easily entangles, and let us run with perseverance the race marked out for us. Let us fix our eyes on Jesus, the author and perfecter of our faith, who for the joy set before him endured the cross, scorning its shame, and sat down at the right hand of the throne of God. Hebrews 12:1–2

These verses from Hebrews 12 come as the climax after chapter 11's long list of believers who, we are told, lived by faith. For some, this list may be intimidating. Possibly some feel these "heroes of faith" are too outstanding as examples to follow. They feel they could not possibly live up to the standards these Old Testament people portrayed.

Our response was quite different. Each name on the list of witnesses provided us with another glimpse of the intersection of divine grace and human broken-ness, and these glimpses sparked our imaginations. For a long time we had been thinking about these people and what they might have looked like. Why not try to take another look by bringing them back to life so we today can be encouraged by them in a fresh way? They were real people just like us, flesh and blood human beings, working, playing, sleeping, sinning, and praying. Their stories are the Bible's story. In their jars of clay we catch glimpses of the glory and faithfulness of the Lord.

Readers browsing through these pages will begin to sense a kinship with these folk, because they are our ancestors, our brothers and sisters in Christ. The Bible, though, does not stop with the Old Testament; it has the New Testament with many more saints blessed by grace as they struggle with the problems of a sinful world.

Finally, the drama of redemption does not stop at the end of bible times. Between those times and our own times (the end times) there have been many, many Christian people who have fought the good fight and paid the ultimate price for the cause of Christ. Their story is also our story.

Please enjoy the book.

Norm Matheis
Syd Hielema

ABRAHAM

Should I tell her, or should I keep this one to myself?

When we left three days ago, Sarah didn't ask any questions. I was often gone for a few days, and the boy is old enough now to accompany me from time to time. I knew what I had to do; I wanted traveling time to give me the words to explain it to her when I returned without him.

But this? "God himself will provide the lamb, son," I had said, remembering how he had provided Isaac. Then came the angel, followed by the ram.

Now I can't think straight anymore. Lord, every time I think that I've come to understand you just a little, you shake my tent poles again. Every time I'd taken matters into my own hands, your hand pulled me back onto your road. This time I followed without asking questions. Am I learning to trust you or am I just too old to fight you now? I don't know.

Must I tell her? Must she be dragged into turmoil again? If I don't tell, he will; then what will I say?

Well, I have three more days to ponder that one.

Cf. *Genesis 22*

JACOB

My father is blind, but he sees it all clearly now. It was two against one, two able-bodied adults against one old blind man. His senses of hearing and touch have become sharper since he lost his eyes, but he dared to trust me more than he trusted his own ears. "The voice is the voice of Jacob, but the hands are the hands of Esau," he had muttered to himself, yet he believed that it was Esau; he trusted that I would not deceive him and he gave Esau's blessing to me.

Oh, but that look in his eyes now! I used the Lord's name to deceive him, and I said it so smoothly—"The Lord gave me success"—when he wondered how I had found an animal to kill and prepare so quickly.

What blasphemy: "The Lord gave me success," hah. What success can come of a blessing obtained through treachery? It was Esau who spoke the truth, "Isn't he rightly named Jacob? He has deceived me."

Must I take this name to the grave? What benefit is it if I gain the whole world yet lose all that I truly hold dear?

Cf. *Genesis 27*

THE MIDWIVES

"Woman—what has man to fear from a woman?" muttered Pharaoh to himself. "It's the male Hebrew babies that I want killed. I can take care of the women." And he ordered us, the Hebrew midwives Shiphrah and Puah, to put the baby boys to death.

Hah, but we would not. "Hebrew women are not like Egyptian women; they are vigorous and give birth before the midwives arrive," we lied.

"You're right," Pharaoh muttered again, "Hebrew women are not like Egyptian women. Egyptian women fear me and obey me. Foolish race that doesn't teach women their proper place. I should have them killed for such disobedience, but—no—they are only women ...."

Exodus 1: 20-21—"So God was kind to the midwives and the people increased and became even more numerous. And because the midwives feared God, he gave them families of their own."

Cf. *Exodus 1*

RAHAB

I am not proud of my life, but I am a survivor. The high and mighty of Jericho find me pleasurable, but they will only allow me to live on the margins, on the city wall, the first expendable one in the event of enemy attack.

Now these foreign men find me useful as well. I know their story; I know how their god has delivered them from Egypt; I know that through the might of their god they have destroyed Sihon and Og and not left one person alive—no, not one. Their god must be a god of great power, far above the gods of Jericho. But these men who serve such a god have entrusted themselves to me! I, Rahab, dweller on the margins, can have these men killed with one word!

I've driven many a hard bargain in my day—could there be one to be made here? No, it cannot be; a god of great power does not need to bargain, does not need to show mercy, but ... I have these men at my mercy! A god of great power does not need people on the margins, but ... these men are here because I am on the margins! I am the one whom the enemy meets first. Could the enemy be my deliverer?

No, I am fooling myself. Now that I have lied to save these men they are no longer at my mercy. They could kill me now and escape through the window tonight. But I know men well, and their eyes do not betray such thoughts. Their eyes are bold, but also honest. Can it be? Could a god of such great power also be a god of trust and mercy? Could a god who makes a great nation out of slaves also deliver me, a foreign woman on the margins?

I do not understand this god; he is not like the gods I have been taught to worship. Maybe not understanding is enough; maybe that is why I can entrust myself to him and his people. Can I?

Cf. *Joshua 2*

JOSHUA

I have seen it all. Miracles too wondrous for the mind to comprehend; rebellion too dark for the heart to carry. I have walked through the sea as on dry ground and drank the water that flowed from the rock. I have trembled before the thunder and smoke surrounding Mt. Sinai and had marveled at the healings of those who looked up to the bronze serpent.

But I have also wept as thousands bowed down to the golden calf. I know the struggles of the human heart and how easily a people are led astray. I have learned the power of leadership and its tremendous effect for good or for ill.

The turning point in my life was my first significant leadership opportunity: spy out the land and report what you find. It was a beautiful land with powerful people, but surely no more powerful than the Egyptians. We had seen how the Lord God had delivered us from Egypt. He would do so again!

That dark day is permanently etched in my mind. Ten of the twelve spies forecast disaster, and their report swayed the nation. O Lord, how could you be faithful to such a people? Will you always be faithful to such a people?

And so, my final speech was no time for sentimentality. It was not a time to beat around the bush. Standing in front of a large stone I cried out my last words: "This stone will be a witness against us. It has heard the words the Lord has said to us. It will be a witness against you if you are untrue to your God."

Cf. *Numbers 13–14, Joshua 24*

SAMSON

I don't mind the soldier. After a few days of getting the mocking out of his system, this sentry has settled down. The sentry knows my past and respects my reputation. I can't see him, and we rarely speak to each other, but there is a silent rapport between us.

It's the women that get to me; I guess it's always been that way. First I hear their voices in the distance and their footsteps shuffling in the sand. Then I can feel their eyes drinking me in, voices tittering and whispering. I know what they're thinking, picturing me with Delilah or one of the others.

From the sounds of their giggling I can imagine their faces, their bodies. And as titillating pictures form in my mind, the knife that put out my eyes cuts into my heart one more time. I was so strong, but I was so weak. I thought I knew my strength, but I did not know my weakness. And now I can see clearly what I could not see with my eyes: I did not know the source of my strength either.

O Lord God of Israel, can your strength visit me once more in my horrible weakness?

Cf. *Judges 13–16, II Corinthians 12: 7–10*

RUTH

Keep on moving, one foot ahead of the other. That was my motto. It began when I married that Hebrew foreigner, and my family began to distance themselves from me. When my husband died, I could read what their eyes were saying, "We could always tell he had no strength in him. Now you're on your own."

It seemed like Naomi had no strength in her either. "Call me Mara," she had said to the townsfolk in Bethlehem, "for the Almighty has made my life very bitter."

But it hadn't always been this way. Naomi had told wondrous stories, stories of Hebrew slaves leaving Egypt, waters parting before them, Pharaoh and his armies drowned in the sea, and a God who had delivered them, the God who made the entire universe. This God was a faithful Father who had led them to this land.

Had Naomi's God changed? I had said to her, "Your people shall be my people, and your God my God." Naomi had changed, but I would cling to the notion that their God did not change, that He was still the faithful One.

So I kept on moving, one foot ahead of the other, gathering the leftover grain from the fields of Boaz. Might this God—Naomi's God, my God—part the waters again someday?

Cf. *the book of Ruth*

DAVID

O Lord, you've helped me through so many battles against so many enemies. From the bear to the lion to Goliath, from Saul to the Philistines to the Ammonites, you've delivered my enemies into my hand every time.

Now, the first time I stay home from that battlefield, I fall—terribly wounded—on a different battlefield, one which I entered without you. Wasn't I due for a sabbatical, Lord? But sabbath without you is no sabbath, no rest. Sabbath without you is a restlessness of the heart and of the body that seeks its rest where no true rest is to be found.

I have been unfaithful, and yet you have promised that your love will never be taken away from me or my house, as it was taken from Saul. You have promised that my throne will be established forever. Hear me Lord as I pray, trusting only in your faithfulness.

> *Have mercy on me, O God, according to your unfailing love;*
> *According to your great compassion, blot out my transgressions.*
> *Wash away all my iniquity and cleanse me from my sin.*
> *For I know my transgressions, and my sin is always before me ....*
> *Create in me a clean heart, O God, and renew a steadfast spirit within me ....*
> *Restore to me the joy of your salvation and grant me a willing spirit, to sustain me ....*
> *The sacrifices of God are a broken spirit;*
> *A broken and contrite heart, O God, you will not despise.*

Cf. II Samuel 11, Psalm 51

ELIJAH

Too much, that's what it was, just plain too much. This God has a funny idea of faithfulness and an even funnier idea of power, but I'm not laughing. I have had enough.

Three years of no rain, that was good. Three years of demonstrating Baal's impotence, Baal's inability to deliver the fertility he promised. And then the crowning triumph: mocking the Baal priests as they pranced and danced and cut themselves and wailed all day long for Baal to show up; dousing the altar with pitchers full of water so that no one could say that the too-dry wood was ripe for burning on its own; and then that fire from heaven consuming the altar and the slaughter of the Baal priests. Yes, Lord, that was faithfulness and power. After that I raced in the rain from the killing fields to Jezreel the capital to proclaim the victory of the Lord.

And now this: fleeing like a hunted jackrabbit to the wilderness, all alone, vulnerable, wanting only to die.

But death did not come. Instead, you came O Lord; fed by angels, spoken to by a still, small voice, given a task to do, told that seven thousand faithful ones remain.

Lord, is that your idea of faithfulness, your idea of power? Lord, following you can be so utterly bewildering, so wild-making.

Cf. *I Kings 17–19*

ESTHER

" ... and if I perish, I perish."

At the mercy of fools, that is what I am. The king is putty in the hands of his advisers, a man who is a boy. Impulsive, easily swayed, eager to please and impress his friends, with no patience for anyone who questions his "wisdom" (what a word!).

Why am I in this God-forsaken place? Mordecai thinks that he has the answer. "And who knows but that you have come to royal position for such a time as this?" he said. Who knows? I smirked when he said that, and as our eyes met we both knew that neither of us dared to say the Name. Could His presence be working through this wicked mess? Would the holy One use my beauty and my seductive charms to tame this foolish beast of a man?

I don't know. We have fasted for three days, and now I will use my intelligence, my cunning, and my beauty to play on the weakness of this man. Am I his friend? Will he be eager to please me?

I don't know if the Lord is in this place or if I must do this one on my own. I no longer remember what the presence of the Lord means. I have heard stories of the temple and descriptions of its beauty; can this palace also be a temple for the Lord's presence? Impossible, I think, but I do not know. I have been taught that the Lord was with Moses in the palace of Pharaoh. Is the Lord of Moses also my Lord?

I do not know, but I will find out. And if I perish, I perish.

Cf. *Esther 5*

JOHN THE BAPTIST

Behold, the Lamb of God who takes away the sin of the world.

Why do you look so shocked? You walked all the way from Jerusalem because you heard about me, the wild man of the Jordan, dressed in camel's hair and eating locusts and wild honey. You walked all that way because you heard about my preaching. I know what they say—"that guy's not afraid of nothin'—he tells Pharisees and Roman soldiers to repent and they even listen to him!" You walked all those miles so you could untie your sandals, soak in the Jordan, and get baptized.

Never mind the camel's hair and the bugs for supper; never mind the repent talk; never mind the baptizing either.

It's about him. I am the voice of one calling in the desert, "make straight the way for the Lord." He is the one who comes after me, the thongs of whose sandals I am not worthy to untie. The reason I came baptizing was that he might be revealed to Israel.

What's that you said? How can a plain looking man be a Lamb? A Lamb of God that takes away the sin of the world? What's that? If many lambs sacrificed in the temple take away the sin of our own people, how can one Jewish man take away the sin of the world?

I don't know. Ask him. He must become greater; I must become less.

Cf. *John 1*

NICODEMUS

"You are Israel's teacher, and you do not understand these things?"

How can he say such a thing! He is so young and so bold, and he seems to fear no one. That is why I came; he doesn't see the danger, and I took pity on him.

But he saw through me. I tried to come as an older and wiser friend, expressing my great respect for him: "Rabbi, we know you are a teacher who has come from God. For no one could perform the miraculous signs you are doing if God were not with him."

He saw that I came to teach him, to instruct him to be more careful, to warn him that the path he was walking on would lead to trouble, perhaps even death.

But before I knew it, he had turned the tables on me: "No one can see the kingdom of God unless he is born again." Born again in order to see? Yes, he confused me, but I am not a fool. I know that he was telling me that I am blind.

And I must be blind. Born of water and the spirit? "The wind blows wherever it pleases." He is right, I am Israel's teacher and I do not understand these things.

But I do understand one thing: God is with that young man in some way. Why and how I cannot tell. What that means and where that will lead, I do not know. But I am sure that it will mean trouble for him.

What does it mean for me?

Cf. *John 3*

THE WOMAN AT THE WELL

Now he's a man different from the others. Our Samaritan men stare at me and Hebrew men turn their heads away as they spit, but he's not like them. And he's certainly better than the seven men I've had so far ....

He asked me for a drink from the well! Why? Others grab the pitcher and motion to me disdainfully to step back while they draw their water. He spoke to me, and even looked at me as he spoke. I was shocked, but I recovered quickly. I'm used to being straight with a man; no sense in beating around the bush. "You are a Jew and I am a Samaritan woman. How can you ask me for a drink?"

Well, then things became strange. "You would have asked me for a drink if you knew who I was," he said. "Living water; whoever drinks the water I give will never thirst again." I thought, "He either has a great sense of humor, or he's crazy, or he's some kind of prophet."

I think he read my mind. He knew all about the men in my life. That answered my question. "Sir, I can see that you are a prophet." I was at least moving in the right direction, so I dropped a hint: "When the Messiah comes, he will explain everything to us." He confirmed my suspicions: "I who speak to you am he."

He spoke to me—words flowing out of him like a river of life, like living water; words that cut to the heart of my dried up soul and soaked it in grace and mercy. He told me everything I ever did—and in the telling set me free.

Cf. *John 4*

THE FATHER OF THE DEMON-POSSESSED BOY

"Everything is possible for him who believes."

That's what he said; it was a declaration, but it came through my ears as a question, perhaps even as an accusation: "Do you believe that I can heal your son?"

Does he really know what it's like? Does he understand what died inside us when we realized that our little child was demon-afflicted all those years ago? Does he know that my wife—locked inside her years of bitterness and grief—refused to come here with me today? Has he heard the other children mock him? Has he seen the child's grandparents refuse to spend time with him? Can he see the reddish lines of exhaustion under my eyes, lines that point to hours of lying awake, staring at blackened walls, can he see them?

But I did come here, walking quickly through the streets with my son whom I love, my son who is so troubled. Why did I come? Was it desperation? Was it the intolerable fear of a future that might even be worse than the past? Did I come in hope? With any sense that just maybe the stories were true, maybe this man does have powers that no one else has, even powers over demons?

"Lord, I do believe! Help me overcome my unbelief!"

Cf. *Mark 9*

WIDOW

Yes, I heard those men talking to their rabbi after I had hurriedly given my two copper coins. "Master," one of them exclaimed, "see how the temple is adorned with beautiful stones and with gifts dedicated to God!"

As the temple reconstruction continues, we all know who's paying for it. We all see the rich placing their large sums in the temple treasury. I understand why that rabbi's disciples are excited. We all long for a temple with the glory of Solomon's; we long for the Lord to come again in power and might, to raise up his children of Israel, to restore the fortunes of Zion.

But my bits of copper will not bring about the revealing of the glory of the Lord. I give only because I cannot not give; the Lord has been faithful to me through all the hard and weary days of my life, and I will be as faithful as I can.

What is the rabbi saying now? He's replying to his disciples' excitement, "As for what you see here, the time will come when not one stone will be left on another; every one of them will be thrown down."

Is he a madman? This building is not even yet finished!

Is he a prophet who delivers the word of the Lord? How can this be? Lord, I have seen and I have known your faithfulness through this temple; this is all I have left, the only anchor to your mercy and neverfailing love. Men despise me for my poverty and my widowhood, but you have not abandoned me. Because of your great love I am not consumed.

How will I know your constancy if this building is demolished? Where will your glory be revealed? Will there be another, a new temple through which I can come to rest in your grace?

I do not know. But I will come and bring my two coins again next week.

Cf. *Luke 21*

JOSEPH OF ARIMATHEA

I heard him preach that day. There was a kindly man who had hung on his every word and had said, "Lord, let me first go and bury my father."

"Let the dead bury their own dead," he had replied, "you follow me."

"Let the dead bury their dead." That was the line that hooked me. Strange words, but I knew what he meant: let nothing come between you and me. For one man it was a dead father. For me it was something else. He had looked into my heart, and he saw how my riches had their hooks into me. That's the kind of rabbi that he was. He knew what lived in a person's heart.

"Do not store up for yourselves treasures on earth, where moth and rust destroy, and where thieves break in and steal. But store up for yourselves treasures in heaven, where moth and rust do not destroy, and where thieves do not break in and steal. For where your treasure is, there your heart will be also."

But where is my treasure now, Jesus, my priceless treasure? Is that him behind me, wrapped in burial cloths? I heard him cry out, "Father, into your hands I commit my spirit." Is he—my treasure—in heaven?

Let the dead bury their own dead? I will bury him. How do I follow a dead Lord? I will bury him. Today that is the only way I know how to love him.

Cf. *John 19*

MARY MAGDALENE

"Mary."

Only he knows my name. One word—one word to identify The Word made flesh, now made flesh again, forever.

"Rabboni."

I know him because he knows me.

One word to identify my teacher, the one who remade me into a new creation, who redeemed my sorry life from the pit.

They didn't know who he was; they said he was demon-possessed. "It is by the prince of demons that he drives out demons," they claimed.

But I know the truth. I know what it is to be demon-possessed, I know what it is to have those evil parasites whisper in your heart, inflict pain upon your body, twist almost-truths into self-stealing lies that suffocate the spirit. I can still hear them hissing and laughing, "You are nothing. Your only value lies in serving men so they can gratify themselves, and, at your age, that won't last much longer." Oh, what darkness, what sordidness, what defeat.

But look! He is all light. His light has shone into my darkness, and the darkness could not overcome it. He has overcome the world!

Three days ago he left; I will never let him leave again. I will cling to him for the rest of my days.

"Do not hold on to me, for I have not yet returned to the Father. Go instead to my brothers and tell them, 'I am returning to my Father and your Father, to my God and your God.'"

"Not yet returned to the Father?" What can that mean? Tell the brothers? They will not believe me; I see how they look at me now still. Lord, I don't understand; Lord, you don't understand...

I will go and tell them the news, because he is the only one who knows my name.

Cf. *John 20*

STEPHEN

"Yes, Lord, telling the story—telling your history—is dangerous business. You commanded Joshua to set up stone monuments so that children would ask, "What do these stones mean?" and their question would lead your people to tell them the story, your history.

Lord, I'm telling your story too, not to children but to the leaders of your body. I told them the story of your faithfulness through Abraham, Isaac, Jacob, Joseph, and Moses. I reminded them how your people rebelled against the leaders you provided for them, rebelled against you. Solomon built the temple, I said, but then I told them, Lord, you can't be contained in a temple. You said it best: "Heaven is my throne and earth is my footstool. What kind of house will you build for me?"

They're not building a house now, but they are erecting a stone monument over my dying body. They are erecting a monument to shut your story down. They'd rather write the history books their way.

But you are the Rock that can never be shaken; when I stand on you, I can never fall.

Look, I see heaven open and the Son of Man standing at the right hand of God!

Lord, Jesus, receive my spirit. Do not hold this sin against them.

Cf. *Acts 7*

CORNELIUS

Why? Why me? Why an angel?

Lord, God of Abraham, Isaac, and Jacob, you know how I love you. You have seen how I have called upon you day after day, the God not only of the Hebrews, but the God who made the heavens and the earth, the God over all. You have blessed me so that I may bless others with your good gifts. You have heard me hungering and thirsting for your presence as a deer longs for running streams. You know that your love fills my heart so that my youth is renewed like the eagles. Yes, I do seek to trust in you, so that you will give me the desires of my heart.

But why did you send the angel? And why did he instruct me to send for a man named Simon who is called Peter? What desires are you growing in my heart that I cannot yet see or feel?

Am I worthy to have this man—Simon who is called Peter—under my roof? When he enters my home, he will be unclean, he will be defiled. Lord, should I not go to him rather than send for him to come to me?

I will wait; I will trust. I will not concern myself with great matters or things too wonderful for me to understand. I will still and quiet my soul like a weaned child with its mother. I will put my hope in the Lord, both now and evermore.

Cf. *Acts 10*

PAUL

House arrest—does it matter? Can anything hinder the coming of the Kingdom of God?

Ever since I was there at Stephen's stoning, I knew he was right. "Look," he had cried out, "I see heaven open and the Son of Man standing at the right hand of God."

I heard his cry; for a time I pretended that I hadn't, but then I couldn't kick against those goads any longer. His dying words have pointed me to Life all these years.

And I've seen it all. I've seen hunger, exhaustion, rejection, discouragement, stoning, whippings, shipwreck, and imprisonment. I've seen deliverance from demons, the dead raised, lives transformed, the body of Christ built up, the power of God.

What's next? Death? A long imprisonment? Freedom? Travels to new lands? More persecution? More demonstrations of the power of God?

It doesn't matter. I know who's standing at the right hand of God. I know that nothing can separate me from the love of God that is in Jesus Christ our Lord. That's enough.

Cf. *Acts 28*

POLYCARP

There are no more words to be said. I have prayed my final prayer, "May I be received this day in thy presence, a sacrifice rich and acceptable." Now the flames will speak: flames driven higher by this unruly mob? Yes, but more truly, flames of the Lord through which I am refined as gold and silver in a furnace. May my body become a delicious fragrance, a sweet-smelling sacrifice that testifies to the Lord's faithfulness and grace.

Eighty-six years I have served the Lord. Nails are not needed to keep me in this place. The Lord has been faithful to me; shall I not be faithful to the end?

The governor advised me to try my arguments for Christ on the crowd. "No," I replied, "it is you whom I thought it might be worth discussing it with, because we have been taught to pay all proper respect to powers and authorities of God's appointment, so long as it does not compromise us. To defend myself to these people would only be a waste of time."

Unruly mobs have crucified our Lord and Savior, stoned his servant Stephen, and taken the lives of many other saints. Now another unruly mob will place me inside that great cloud of witnesses that has gone on before. Like my brother Stephen, I will fix my eyes upon Jesus, as I know that his hand is forever on me.

Polycarp (69? – 155?) served as the bishop of Smynra until his martyrdom.

MONICA

"Pray without ceasing." Surely those words tell us that St. Paul was well aware of two deep truths: the hardness of the human heart and the deeply faithful grace of our Lord. We may resist Him year after year, but He does not give up, and therefore we do not give up.

But there is another—a third—deep truth that impresses me especially this day: the weariness of the heart that is enjoined to pray without ceasing. Oh Lord, I've said it all so many times and you've seen it all so many times. I have brought before your throne my husband Patricius and my son Augustine, but their lives remain testimonies to the kingdom of darkness.

Yes, my son has a brilliant mind, admired by many, but of what use is it? He may speak in the tongues of men or of angels and be able to fathom many mysteries with much knowledge, but without the love of Christ it is all useless. No, it is worse than useless. A brilliant mind in the service of darkness is a terrible thing.

Oh Lord, today I do not pray for them, my husband and my son. Today I pray only with my own tears. I feel as if I can pray without ceasing no more. My tears have become my food day and night. My heart is faint within me. My eyes see only barriers on the road ahead, and I cannot go on.

Lord, remember my son of tears, remember my tears.

Monica (333–387) is remembered as the mother of Augustine, one of the greatest Christian leaders of the early church period.

ST. FRANCIS

"Look at the birds of the air; they do not sow or reap or store away in barns, and yet your heavenly Father feeds them. Are you not much more valuable than they? Who of you by worrying can add a single hour to his life?"

Oh Lord Jesus, you make it sound so easy, just as those birds make it look so easy. Were you thinking of a man like me when you taught those words? Does your teaching cover my burden?

I was to be a knight, a great warrior, the son of a wealthy merchant who would return victorious from battle to rest in luxury. But no, on the way to my second battle you told me in a dream to turn around and go home. Yes, I obeyed, only to be mocked by family and friends as a coward and a fool: a coward for fleeing from battle, and a fool for rejecting a life of riches.

What now? Am I to look at the birds of the air for direction? Will these tiny creatures reveal to me what my family and friends do not know? You, Lord, instructed me to take off my knight's armor. As you feed the birds of the air, will you also feed me with further instruction concerning the road ahead? If I am much more valuable than they, will you not also provide what I need when all others have rejected me?

My deepest desires are not concerned with adding a single hour to my life. Rather, I crave a single-heartedness, complete devotion to you, my master. Can the birds of the air show me that way? They seem so scattered, so mindless, so empty of devotion of any kind.

Pour your peace upon me, Lord, I pray, and make me too a channel of your peace.

Francis of Assisi (1181–1226) embraced a life of poverty and serving the poor.

CATHERINE OF SIENA

For Christ's sake, I delight in weaknesses, in insults, in hardships, in persecutions, in difficulties. For when I am weak, then I am strong. Your power is made perfect in weakness.

Oh Lord, rid my body of its pain! I long to depart and escape this dying prison and its unceasing torment. If disease will not bring about my end, I pray that the sword will—that the battles I wage on behalf of the poor and needy will claim my life below as it lifts up theirs.

Precious Savior, you have shown me visions of your indescribable splendor and you have shown me scenes of the deep suffering of your children. Why do the poor and weak continue to be oppressed while the rich and mighty continue to do wrong? How can those who lead your church seem so callous, so indifferent? Do you not see the letters that I write day by day, the calls that I send forth for your church to be renewed and its leaders to repent and serve you in truth and justice? How long, O Lord, how long must we wait?

Lord, I long to depart and be with you, but perhaps it is better for me to remain and fight, though my body can hardly go on. But I see you, Lord, the Lamb led to the slaughter, a sheep silent before her shearers, crushed for our iniquities, crushed for my iniquities.

My suffering is nothing when set before yours. I will go on, as long as you lend me breath. I will fix my eyes on Jesus, who for the joy set before him endured the cross. I will consider him who endured such opposition from sinful men, so that I will not grow weary and lose heart.

Catherine of Siena (1347–1380) cared for the sick and became an adviser to both church and civic leaders.

MICHELANGELO

Time to think, that's what I've always had, time to think. Maybe too much time to think. Hour upon hour, day after day. Chipping at marble or dabbing at the ceiling, my work is slow, laborious, even tedious. My hand has become slow, but my mind continues to whirl. There is too much to ponder, too much that cannot be understood, mysteries too great for the human mind to comprehend.

Oh yes, once I knew so much more than I know today. I knew the face of beauty, I knew the mind of truth, I knew the shape of goodness. I was clear-eyed and bold, strong and handsome, able to confront and challenge; I knew the high ideals of humanity and was able to give them visible shape and form. Like my David behind me, the world was at my grasp; I felt as if I held it in my power. Yes, once I knew it all, once I had it all.

But now I have lost my David, and I catch—oh—just a fleeting glimpse of David the child of God. I see the David I could not see, and though I see him but dimly, his song is becoming my song: "My heart is not proud, O Lord, my eyes are not haughty; I do not concern myself with great matters, or things too wonderful for me. But I have stilled and quieted my soul; like a weaned child with its mother, like a weaned child is my soul within me. O Israel, put your hope in the Lord, both now and evermore."

Can a man become a child when he is old? Yes, he can; yes, I am. Oh, I know so little now, but I do know this: "I work out of love for God and I put all my hope in him."

Michelangelo (1475–1564) was the most famous artist of the Italian Renaissance.

BLAISE PASCAL

"Jesus Christ is the end of all, and the centre to which all tends. Whoever knows him knows the reason of everything." (*Pensees*, Book eight)

I will not forget your Word, O Lord. How can I? It addresses us every day in every way. I see you in mathematics and physics, the beauty of geometry, the laws of hydraulics. The vastness and wonder of your creation arouses my reason and impresses me with its boundaries. The foolishness of those who claim to know so much and yet know nothing! Without Jesus Christ all knowledge is but a sounding gong and a clanging cymbal. "What a vast distance there is between knowing God and loving him .... Human things must be known to be loved: but Divine things must be loved to be known."

What is my body? Almost killed in an accident—an accident that drew me to you, my Lord. Always in pain, wracked by illness, crippled. Yet you are the God of Abraham, God of Isaac, God of Jacob, my Lord and my God. What is pain before the wonder that you are?

And what is man before you? They call me a heretic; they say I am stubborn, loud, overbearing. What does it matter? Their reasoning does not point to the Lord, the One who knows the reason of everything. Their ends are not your end. Their words can be forgotten; but I will never forget your Word, O Lord.

Blaise Pascal (1623–1662) was a French philosopher, mathematician, and scientist.

GEORGE FREDERICK HANDEL

"I did think I did see all heaven before me, and the great God himself."

Oh Lord, my eyes are weary! My eyes have rejoiced in Hallelujahs, visions of the Lord God omnipotent reigning, and the kingdom of this world that has become the kingdom of our Lord. My ears have heard rank upon rank of angels singing out "Hallelujahs" to the Lamb, and their echoes resounding from the saints below. My eyes are weary from beholding glories too great for the tongue to tell.

But my eyes have seen more. My eyes have seen the paltriness and pettiness of human scheming and deceit. I too have been despised and rejected, a man of sorrows and acquainted with griefs. I too have been laughed to scorn. Why do jealousy, envy, resentment, and revenge reign so easily on the throne the Lamb has claimed? Why are the Lord's creatures so quick to surrender the glory of the Lord for the weakness of humankind?

But I know that my Redeemer liveth, and that he shall stand upon the earth one day. Someday worms will destroy my body. This day it seems they are seeking to destroy my soul. But in my flesh I have seen the living God.

Worthy is the Lamb that was slain to receive power and riches and wisdom and strength and honor and glory and blessing. My eyes long for the day when they can proclaim your worthiness without end, without weariness, without a blurring of vision. Until that day, if God be for us, who can be against us? Who shall lay anything to the charge of God's elect? It is God that justifieth; it is Christ who is at the right hand of God who makes intercession for us, for me.

Hallelujah!

George Frederick Handel (1685–1759) was one of the best-known German composers of the Baroque era.

SOJOURNER TRUTH

"That man over there says that women need to be helped into carriages and lifted over ditches, and to have the best place everywhere. Nobody ever helps me into carriages, or over mud-puddles, or gives me any best place! And ain't I a woman? Look at me! Look at my arm! I have ploughed and planted and gathered into barns, and no man could head me! And ain't I a woman? I could work as much, and eat as much as a man —when I could get it—and bear the lash as well! And ain't I a woman? I have borne thirteen children, and seen them most all sold off to slavery, and when I cried out with a mother's grief, none but Jesus heard me! And ain't I a woman?"

"That little man in black there, he says women can't have as much rights as men, 'cause Christ wasn't a woman! Where did your Christ come from? Where did your Christ come from? From God and a woman! Man had nothing to do with Him."

Oh Lord, I'm weary and I want to rest. My child had been stolen from me and I took the white man to court and won him back. I've been accused of murder and acquitted. My arm has been wrestled out of my shoulder socket as "I've traveled up and down the land, showing people their sins, and being a sign to them." Yea, crowds come to listen and victories are won, but O Lord, I'm tired and I want to rest.

But Lord, I'm too angry to rest! As long as black people are treated differently than white people and women are treated differently than men, how can I rest? There's no rest when there's still wickedness; there's no rest for me, Lord, just like there was no place for the son of man to lay his head.

"If the first woman God ever made was strong enough to turn the world upside down all alone, these women together ought to be able to turn it back and get it right-side up again. And now that they are asking to do it, the men better let them."

"Obliged to you for hearing me, and now Old Sojourner ain't got nothing more to say."

(The "Ain't I a woman" speech was given at the 1851 Women's Rights Convention in Akron, Ohio.) Sojourner Truth (1797–1883) was an abolitionist and women's rights advocate who was herself freed from slavery in 1827.

PIETJE BALTUS

I had to tell him.

After I told my father I could not go to church to listen to that preacher and his modern, shallow sermons, father replied, "That's fine. You stay home; but you must tell the preacher why you are staying home. When he notices that you are not attending the services he will come. Then you must tell him."

He came, and I did tell him. "Dominee Kuyper," I said, "you are welcome here, but I cannot shake your hand. You know many things about the Bible, but you do not know Jesus. You know many things about the message, but you do not know the Messenger. We do not need to be impressed by your great knowledge. We need to be fed the Word of the Lord. Your name may be Abraham, but you are not leading us in the line of Abraham, Isaac, and Jacob. I cannot come to worship at the altar of knowledge without the heart. I cannot listen to your empty sermons."

I hardly believed I had said those words, but father said I must tell him the truth. The dominee was speechless; he was not angry and he did not argue or defend himself. He looked stunned, paralyzed, like an ungreased windmill that suddenly freezes to a stop on a blustery day. "Good day," he said, and left without another word.

When father returned home from church this morning, he was very quiet, and he looked at me thoughtfully for some time. I gave him the coffee I had prepared, and we sat down. He shook his head. "I don't know," he said, "I don't know. Something was different this time, but I'm not sure what. The dominee almost looked helpless on the pulpit, almost as if he was the congregation and we were the preacher. I don't know what to think."

I know what to think. I had to tell him, and I'm glad that I did. What happens now is out of my hands.

Pietje Baltus (1830–1914) was a member of the first congregation served by Abraham Kuyper (theologian, politician) in Beesd, the Netherlands. Kuyper began his ministry there in 1863.

DIETRICH BONHOEFFER

By the Powers for Good (December 1944)

The forces for good in wonder surround us,
Through faith and peace they'll guard and guide.
And so these days with you I'll live,
With you, my friends, a new year abide.

The year just past still lingers in our hearts,
And evil times on us their burdens weigh,
O Lord, to shaken souls bestow your peace,
Your promised grace, your solace, this bleak day.

But should you tend your cup of sorrow,
To drink the bitter dregs at your command,
We accept with thanks and without trembling,
This offering from your gracious, loving hand.

But if joy be once again your gift bestowed,
To this our world with sunlit skies so fair,
May we always hearken to these days of old,
And commit our lives to your loving care.

May your waxen candles flaming spread their warmth,
As their glow flickers darkness into the light.
May your will be done to make us one again;
May your love's glimmering hope illumine our night.

When now the silence spreads around us,
O let us hear the sounds you raise,
Of world unseen in growth abounding,
And children chanting hymns of praise.

The forces for good surround us in wonder,
They firm up our courage for what comes our way,
God's with us from dawn to the slumber of evening,
The promise of love at the break of each day.

"By the Powers for Good" was written by Dietrich Bonhoeffer (1906–1945), a German pastor, theologian, and seminary professor who was hanged at a concentration camp in Flossenburg, Germany on April 9, 1945 for participating in a plot to assassinate Adolf Hitler.